-HERGÉ-

THE ADVENTURES OF TINTIN

THE BLUE LOTUS

EGMONT

Reproduction of the first colour edition published in 1946
Text adapted from the 1983 translation by Leslie Lonsdale-Cooper and Michael Turner
Artwork copyright © 1946 Casterman
Text copyright © 2008 Egmont UK Limited
This edition first published in Great Britain 2008 by Egmont UK Limited
239 Kensington High Street, London W8 6SA
ISBN 978 1 4052 4070 3
Printed in China
10 9 8 7 6 5 4 3 2 1

THE BLUE LOTUS

藍蓮花

NEWS OF TINTIN

TINTIN AND SNOWY are in India, guests of the Maharaja of Gaipajama, enjoying a well-earned rest. The evil gang of international drug-smugglers, encountered in *Cigars of the Pharaoh*, has been smashed and its members are behind bars. With one exception. Only the mysterious gang leader is unaccounted for: he disappeared over a cliff.

But questions have still to be answered. What of the terrible Rajaijah juice, the 'poison of madness'? Where were the shipments of opium going, hidden in the false cigars? And who really was the mastermind behind the operation?

CRR WHEEE

How can a dog get a wink of sleep? Not a minute's peace since he fell for short-wave radio!...

CRR WHEEE WHUIIT CRR

There it is again. That's the station I've been trying to identify...

It doesn't make any sense... What can it possibly mean?

RRCQ 15.30 direct special attention charles yokohama urgently going oddly slow istanbul ten nasty gaps in saturday means tibetan medicine easily changes west ekombe

It must have some meaning ...but what?

My direction-finder shows WSW, ENE. In theory the transmitter should be along a line in the same direction, passing through Gaipajama.

Tintin Sahib, the Maharaja requests your presence.

Thank you. I'll come.

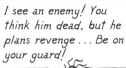

I see an enemy! You think him dead, but he plans revenge... Be on your guard!

I also see a fakir, a disgrace to our brotherhood, dedicated to your downfall. He is close to you... very close to you. He spies upon you... He has a terrible weapon... and there is no defence.

Beware... I see another man... a man with a yellow skin... His hair is black... He wears glasses ... Take every care! He has sworn to destroy you!

Tintin Sahib, there is a stranger in the gallery, asking for you. He says he has come from Shanghai to see you.

From Shanghai?

From Shanghai? That's a fair distance... just to talk to me... How peculiar.

Mr Tintin, sir?

Me? Yes...

Yellow skin ... black hair ... glasses ... Careful, Tintin!

I have something extremely important to tell you. Can we talk here?

Certainly. We're quite alone: look...

哇

?

A dart... dipped in Rajaijah juice... the poison of madness?!

He's gone... He didn't waste any time...

Quick! Speak! What have you to tell me?

I... I... Yes... I remember.

Mitsuhirato... Someone needs you... I... Shanghai ... Remember that name, Mitsuhirato... Mitsu... Mitsuhirato.

Good. Then?

TONG SI NAN PEI

Poor fellow! ... He's gone mad! ...

TINTIN!

!

The other fakir, Tintin, the one I sent to prison, the one with the poisoned darts, he's escaped . . .

I thought as much!

Look . . . the poison of madness!

WOOAH!

WOOAH!

By Brahma! How awful! . . .

I must go to China at once . . . Poor chap . . . he just had time to tell me I'm needed in Shanghai.

We must pack the trunk, quickly . . .

. . . I see an enemy! . . . You think him dead, but he plans revenge . . .

Well, we'll soon see!

Hello, where has Snowy gone?

Snowy? . . . Snowy? . . .

Snowy!

SNOWY!

Great snakes! . . . He can't have been kidnapped!

You haven't seen Snowy?

Snowy? . . . No . . .

You search over there . . . . I'll go this way . . .

Nothing, Sahib . . .

We haven't found him.

'They' must have taken him!

Some hours later . . .

They're bringing your trunk down . . . You've really made up your mind to go?

Yes . . . and no . . . I can't go without Snowy . . .

4

BING
BANG
BOOM

Snowy!! My poor Snowy! . . . I must have shut you in the trunk! . . . Well, now we can go!

Goodbye! . . . Good luck!

Goodbye . . .

Some time later . . .

So this is Shanghai . . .

That's him! That's him all right!

No mistake, that's him.

CONTINENT HOTEL

Mitsuhirato . . . Mitsuhirato . . . But how do we find him? . . . It's certainly a Japanese name, but . . .

Come in!

RAT
TAT
TAT

'TO MR TINTIN' . . . Most peculiar! . . . How does anyone know I'm here yet . . .

Mr Tintin,
the news of your arrival fills me with joy. I cannot convey my happiness at the prospect of gazing upon your noble and virtuous features.
May I humbly beg the privilege of calling upon you at 3 o'clock this afternoon? My servant will await your gracious reply

Mitsuhirato

Street of Tranquil

Excellent! . . . Please tell the messenger his master is too kind. He mustn't put himself out. I will call upon him myself.

I wonder how our Mr Mitsuhirato knew I was here . . . Anyway, he's certainly a man with impeccable manners . . .

Are Japanese good chaps, Tintin?

Mr Mitsuhirato, Street of Tranquillity . . .

得罪!
先生！

Dirty little Chinaman! . . . To barge into a white man!

Thank you, sir, thank you for saving me.

Mr Tintin, sir . . .

Show him in . . .

My dear Mr Tintin, you must go back to India at once. The Maharaja of Gaipajama is in great danger. I sent a Chinese messenger to tell you to guard the Maharaja. Didn't you see him?

Yes, but he was struck by a poisoned dart and only managed to say two words: your name and Shanghai. Then . . . nonsense . . .

Despicable creatures! Such persons stop at nothing! Believe me, you were wrong to leave the Maharaja. Who knows what they will do in your absence? . . .

Who are 'they'?

Please pardon me, I cannot tell you more: my own life would be in danger . . . But I beg you to take heed and go back to India.

I see . . . thank you. Maybe I'll take the next boat back. Meanwhile I'll telegraph the Maharaja to be on his guard.

Excellent plan . . . Ah, I was forgetting. Beware of everyone here, and especially the Chinese. Your life hangs by a thread . . .

But . . . how do you know? . . .

A true Japanese knows everything, honourable sir.

Bit seedy round here, eh?

Yes, I'm inclined to agree!

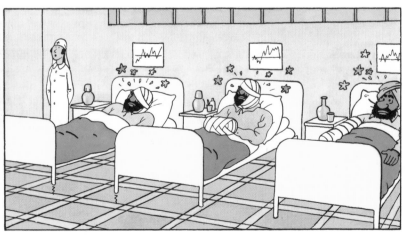

Obviously they knew I was innocent. And yet ... they didn't go after the attacker ...

A telegram for you, Mr Tintin, and a letter, and this parcel ...

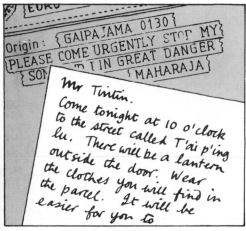

Origin: GAIPAJAMA 0130
PLEASE COME URGENTLY STOP MY SON ... T I N GREAT DANGER (MAHARAJA)

Mr Tintin.
Come tonight at 10 o'clock to the street called T'ai p'ing lu. There will be a lantern outside the door. Wear the clothes you will find in the parcel. It will be easier for you to

All very mysterious ... What's going on now?

Poisoned? ... No, thank goodness! His heart's still beating ... He's asleep ... Drugged? ...

The tea! ... He must have drunk the tea I spilt on the floor ... But ... But ...

BANG

That shot ... it was providential! ... If I'd drunk the tea ...

You sleep it off, Snowy old fellow. And don't worry if I'm late back ...

T'ai p'ing lu? ...

Here we are ... Not a very healthy-looking place ...

RAT TAT TAT

You saw? . . . They made the signal!

We'll have a look . . .

Here are the boxes . . .

There, the sampan is coming back.

The next morning . . .

What do you make of it, Snowy? . . . Last night, sailing to Bombay. This morning here in this room . . . . . .

Anyway, where exactly are we? . . .

We'll very soon find out . . .

RAT TAT TAT

Aha! There's someone who'll be able to tell us . . .

Excuse me, sir . . .

THE MADMAN! SHANGHAI! . . .

Have you found the way? . . . No? . . . Good! . . . Then I'll cut off your head! . . .

Again! . . .

16

Didi! . . . Stop that! . . .

Leave us . . . and behave!

Yes, Papa . . .

Allow me to introduce myself: Wang Chen-yee. I am the father of the poor soul you saw just now. He was attacked by our enemies and lost his mind the night he arranged to meet you in Shanghai. He was guarding you.

CRACK

BANG

So it was him!

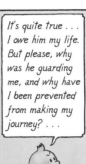

It's quite true . . . I owe him my life. But please, why was he guarding me, and why have I been prevented from making my journey? . . .

Certainly, I owe you an apology for such a violent kidnapping. But the telegram recalling you to India was false. My son was to explain, the night you saw him, and to ask you to stay longer in Shanghai. Alas, he was unable to do so, and you set sail. But you must remain in China . . .

I must remain in China? . . . But why? . . .

Will you come with me? . . . You will understand . . .

You stay here, Snowy, and behave yourself!

Here is the friend who will be of infinite help . . .

Now, Mr Tintin, it is time to give you an explanation . . .

These are the headquarters of the Sons of the Dragon. We are a secret society dedicated to the fight against opium, the terrible drug causing such havoc in our country. Our greatest adversary is a Japanese, with whom you are acquainted. He is named Mitsuhirato . . .

Mitsuhirato? . . .

Well, well! Why don't I practise on him?

What does he want with me?

Yes, Mitsuhirato. He's a Japanese secret agent in China ... and at the same time, one of the most active and evil of men ...

Hello, Tokyo?

SHIP	CARGO	DESTINATION
MARIGOLD	OPIUM	MARSEILLES
	OPIUM	ANTWERP
	OPIUM	LE HAVRE
BLACK STAR	OPIUM	ROTTERDAM
EVEREST	OPIUM	HAMBURG
SATURN	OPIUM	LIVERPOOL

... Not content with spying, he has joined forces with opium smugglers ... He helps them distribute all over the world, but mostly here in China.

Hello? ... Hello? Tokyo here ... Ah, it's you ...

Yes, Excellency ... All is well ... Tintin? ... On the way to India ... recalled by telegram, sent by me, of course ... No, not easy ... Those meddling Sons of the Dragon tried to keep him here ... I had to take extreme measures ...

Perfect! ... Now the coast is clear for ... you know what. Succeed in that ... and you will receive the Order of Fujiyama, first class!

I'm certain to succeed, Excellency, provided your propaganda is well organised ... It will be? ... That is good! ... Goodbye then, Excellency ...

We hoped you would be willing to help us, so we sent a messenger to India ... But Mitsuhirato's spy network is excellent. They attacked the messenger and he went mad ... Yet you still came, and ...

WOOAH! WOOAH!

That's Snowy!

Snowy! ... He's gone!

I'm going to help you to find the way. Don't worry, there's nothing to it ... It just means cutting off your head ...

Look how sharp the blade is ...

We'll go and look in my son's room . . .

Didi! . . .

RAT TAT TAT TAT

Come in, Father, and see an interesting experiment . . .

And never do that again!

Good to be together again, eh Snowy?

Forgive my poor son, Mr Tintin. He isn't responsible for his actions . . .

Courage, Mr Wang. I'll do all I can to find an antidote to that terrible poison . . .

Now, when Mitsuhirato had failed to stop you coming to China, he tried to scare you into leaving immediately. When you stayed, he tried to kill you. Now he believes you are on the way back to India. So far so good. We know he communicates by radio with his accomplices . . .

By radio? . . . Well, well . . . What a pity my receiving set is in my trunk aboard the 'Ranchi' . . . I could have . . .

Your trunk came with you, dear friend. We would not wish to deprive you of your luggage . . .

Look . . . One day in Gaipajama I intercepted this peculiar message: 'Direct special attention Charles Yokohama urgently going oddly slow Istanbul ten nasty gaps in Saturday means Tibetan medicine easily changes West Ekombe'. I couldn't make head or tail of it . . .

Then, on my journey, I managed to solve it. Take the first two letters of each word, and that gives you: 'Dispatch your goods. Listen again same time each week.'

The word Yokohama made me think the sender of the message was Japanese and . . . Wait! A signal on the same wavelength . . .

blizzard
ueda
location
tuesday
storm
entraps
top nine
ghurkas
T

Take the first two letters of each word . . . there . . . 'Blue Lotus ten tonight' . . . Well, that doesn't make much more sense . . .

Blue lotus . . . Blue lotus . . . Wait . . . Yes, I know . . . In Shanghai there's an opium den with that name . . .

An opium den? Right! I'll be there tonight . . .

That night, at ten o'clock . . .

THE BLUE LOTUS

No, Mr Mitsuhirato has not yet arrived. But he won't be long. Please come with me.

I'll wait for him here . . .

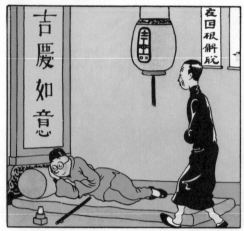

Good evening, sir. Someone is waiting for you . . .

Yes, I know.

!

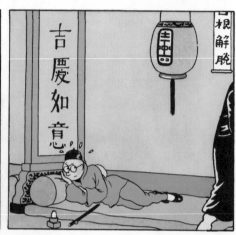

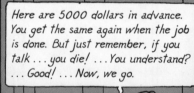

Here are 5000 dollars in advance. You get the same again when the job is done. But just remember, if you talk . . . you die! . . . You understand? . . . Good! . . . Now, we go.

Good night, master.

Get in . . .

The car! If I can reach it . . .

Suffering Samurais! . . . Tintin!

Ministry of War Tokyo Stop Chinese bandits have blown up Shanghai-Nanking railway . . .

Damage to property not significant Stop

Not significant! We'll soon see about that . . .

This is Radio Tokyo! . . . The effrontery of Chinese guerrillas knows no bounds! News just in details a treacherous attack on the Shanghai-Nanking railway . . .

. . . Having blown up the track, the brigands . . .

. . . stopped the train and attacked innocent passengers . . .

. . . Reports tell of many killed trying to defend themselves.

Twelve Japanese died. After the attack . . .

. . . the bandits, numbering more than a hundred, fled with their loot.

Tokyo Express! . . . Special! . . . Special! . . . Chinese bandits attack passenger train! . . . Many dead . . . Read all about it!

. . . Japan must never forget her duty as the guardian of law and civilisation in the Far East . . . Glory to our brave soldiers who have now gone to defend this noble cause! . . .

. . . and once again Japan has fulfilled her mission as guardian of law and civilisation in the Far East! . . . If we have been forced, to our utmost regret, to send troops into China, it is for the good of China herself!

LEAGUE OF NATIONS

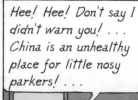
Hee! Hee! Don't say I didn't warn you! . . . China is an unhealthy place for little nosy parkers! . . .

Tintin should have been back long ago . . .

Where in the world can he be?

My driver will take you back to Shanghai . . . I have unfinished business with our young friend!

They've brought me here and locked me in . . . What will they do next?

My dear Mr Tintin, do forgive me for not paying attention to you sooner . . .

Well, what are you going to do with me?

I'm going to enjoy myself, dear friend. Here on the outskirts of Shanghai no one saw you arrive, and no one will ever see you leave, if that's what I decide.

You are at my mercy. If I so wish, you will vanish! . . . But all things considered, I don't want to kill you. No, on the contrary. I've decided to let you go . . .

!

Excuse me . . . I'll be back in a moment . . .

I . . . of course . . . As you wish . . .

I must say, I hadn't expected this . . .

Do you know what this is? . . .

The poison of madness!!!

Just one little jab . . . and I'll set you free . . .

Don't be afraid! . . . Only a little dose . . . We don't want to overdo things!

There! . . . You see . . . It didn't take long . . .

Mad! . . . I'm going to go mad!

And Chang? . . . He's still not back either?

No, Venerable, not yet.

Whatever happens, I simply must find Tintin! . . .

Each ♪ peach ♪ pear ♪ plum ♪ In ♪ comes ♪♪ Tom ♪♪ Thumb! . . . ♪♪♪

And now, my little man, out you go!

Chick . . . chick . . . chick . . . chicken!

Seven suffering Samurais! That's not Rajaijah... So what did I...?

Chang went to watch the house of Mitsuhirato, Venerable... He has returned...

Send him here at once!

I was hidden in the next room. I put coloured water in place of the Rajaijah, and I've brought you the real poison. I took care of his knife and his gun too...

I'll soon find him. He can't have gone far...

There!!...

! CLICK

?

I could have sworn my gun was loaded... Anyway, I still have my knife!...

Kamikaze! The blade's made of rubber!

!
!

And perhaps that's made of rubber as well!...

An hour later...

Major, I'm Japanese... I've been half murdered by a young European, a Chinese spy! His name is Tintin!

Now we must go back to Mr Wang...

5000 YEN REWARD TINTIN SPY

!

There isn't a moment to lose... I must get out of the city...

Too late! Japanese patrols are watching the gates. I can't get past!...

How to escape from the city?...

?

You're the one with a Japanese price on your head!

26

27

So? . . . You are sure of your facts?

Absolutely certain, Major . . . I saw him clearly as I'm seeing you!

If we walk fast we'll be back with Mr Wang by tonight.

Lucky for me I was hidden. I'd better keep an eye open in case he returns . . .

Careful! Here comes that armoured car again!

We didn't find him, sir. Not a chance of his escaping along that road . . .

At last! . . . I thought I'd never see you again!

You lied! . . . We found no trace of Tintin . . . You will be detained . . . And mark my words: no one plays the fool with the military authority! . . .

But . . . but . . . I . . .

Just let me get out of here and I'll show him what I'm made of, the little swine!

So this is the mysterious poison that's done so much damage . . . and if it hadn't been for your servant I'd have been a victim, too . . .

AYAYAH! OHO! YOUP! ? ?

YAAH HI!

Our son is having another fit of madness, Wang. Please, try to calm him!

Poor, poor Mrs Wang . . .

If only someone could do something to cure his madness, but that's impossible . . .

Unless . . . yes, but it's only a chance in a million . . .

And if I do that, I'll have to get back through the Japanese lines . . .

Don't cry, Mrs Wang . . . Tomorrow morning I'll go to Shanghai and I'll have that poison analysed. Who knows, perhaps we may find a cure for your son's madness.

Next morning . . .

I fear for you. Don't forget there is a price on your head!

Don't be afraid . . . If I can manage to reach the International Settlement, I'll be safe. They can't do anything to me there . . .

Hello? . . . Yes, speaking . . . To whom have I the honour . . .

Dawson here, Chief of Police of the International Settlement . . . I believe you're holding a chap called Gibbons . . . Yes . . . From a large American company . . . I think you'd be wise to let him go . . . Could make an awful lot of trouble . . .

Agreed, but on one condition . . . We're looking for a spy, name of Tintin. If he takes refuge in the International Settlement, you'll hand him over . . .

It's a deal, Major . . . You can count on me!

Full of charm, isn't he? And that's our new general!

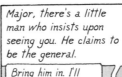
Major, there's a little man who insists upon seeing you. He claims to be the general.

Bring him in. I'll give him 'general'!

But . . . but the general has just left!

And I'm telling you, blockhead, that I'M General Haranochi! . . . I was attacked on the road by a young Chinese who stripped me of my uniform!! . . .

No one about? . . . Good!

Here we go! . . .

One . . .

Two . . .

And three!

Now let's release my false stomach . . . All right, Snowy?

Now to the International Settlement . . . And make it snappy!

All's well. We made it!

Halt! . . . Your papers!

My identity papers? . . . I'm afraid I haven't got them with me . . . But my name's Tintin and I . . .

Sorry! . . . Nothing doing!

But look! You can see I'm a European . . .

Nothing doing!

Please . . .

What's the problem?

The boy hasn't any papers, sir . . .

No use arguing, sonny. Must have proper papers to enter the Settlement . . .

Now what? . . . Crumbs! A Japanese patrol! I must get in. If I don't . . .

* See Cigars of the Pharaoh

33

Is Professor Fang Hsi-ying at home please?

Honourable master has not yet returned. But he will not be long. Will you wait?

My heart is anxious. Honourable master told me he would be home by ten o'clock. Now it is after midnight . . .

Do you know where he went?

Yes, he went to a reception given in his honour by his friend Mr Liu Ju-lin in the Street of the Purple Mountain.

Then I'll go there . . .

What? My honourable friend has not reached home? . . . Strange . . . He left at about ten o'clock with one of our guests, Mr Rastapopoulos.

Rastapopoulos, here? . . . Where is he staying?

The Palace Hotel, quick! . . .

Come in!

RAT TAT TAT

Good evening, Mr Rastapopoulos!

Tintin! What a pleasant surprise! . . .

I've just come from Mr Liu. He said you left his house with Professor Fang Hsi-ying. Is that right? . . .

Yes, quite right. I gave the professor a lift in my car and left him at the corner of the Street of Infinite Wisdom, where he lives . . . Why do you ask?

Professor Fang Hsi-ying never got home.

Didn't get home? . . . But it's only a few steps to his door from the place where I dropped him . . .

34

Hello? . . . Yes, it's me . . . What is it? . . . What?!! You didn't arrest him? . . . Dozy dolt!

It wasn't my fault, Chief. The porter didn't warn me soon enough. He'd already gone . . .

Next morning . . .

Your master still hasn't come home? . . . Very odd . . . Well, I'll see what I can do . . .

Thank you!

Let's go over the professor's route from the time he got out of Rastapopoulos's car . . .

Aha! A patch of oil . . . A car must have parked here. I'm certain someone was waiting for the professor and grabbed him . . .

OH!

Wooah!

W.R. GIBBONS
Director
AMERICAN & CHINESE STEEL INCORPORATED
NEW YORK   SHANGHAI
53, Bund   Shanghai

Gibbons . . . I don't know that name.

He didn't wish to give his name, sir, but he told me he'd only be a minute . . .

OK. Let him in . . .

Please come in . . .

TIME IS MONEY

Mr Gibbons, this is your business card, isn't it? . . . Well, I found it in the Street of Infinite Wisdom near the house of Professor Fang Hsi-ying . . . He disappeared last night . . .

Disappeared? . . . That's news to me . . . Funny, I met him last evening . . . Gave him my card . . .

He seemed worried . . .

TIME IS MONEY

Street of Infinite Wisdom . . . Fang Hsi-ying . . .

Hello! . . . Hello! . . . Get me the Chief of Police! Fast!

Hello? . . . Richards? Take Brown and go to the Fang Hsi-ying house on the Street of Infinite Wisdom. Tintin is on his way there. Handcuff him and bring him here!

Fang Hsi-ying's house! . . . At the double! . . .

POLICE

Oh, it is you, sir! ... Come, please! ... I have just received a letter from Honourable Master!

A letter?

Dear Chen,
I have been seized by Chinese gangsters demanding a ransom of 50,000 dollars. It is essential the police do not look for them. If they are alarmed they will kill me.
The ransom is to be left, within a fortnight, at the old temple about an hour's journey from Hukow on the right bank of the Yangtze Kiang. As I do not possess sufficient money

I'm going to look for the Professor ... While I'm gone will you look after this package? ... Please, take the greatest care of it ...

OK, Chief, we got Tintin for you.

Well done, Richards ... Bring him in ...

I'd like to know why you've arrested me ...

Just a second, old man, and you'll be in the picture ...

Hello? ... Japanese border post? ... Is that you, Major? ... Dawson here ...

Yes ... yes ... Tintin! ... You arrested him? ... Congratulations! ... Yes, that's right ... Excellent ... In half an hour ... Goodbye ...

It's disgraceful! ... I'm on international territory here and you have no right to hand me over to the Japanese! ...

Excuse me, you're quite wrong ... Have you papers allowing you to be in the Settlement? ... No, you haven't ... So I have the right to expel you ... If the Japanese arrest you, that's none of my business ...

Half an hour later ...

NOTICE

Hello . . . yes . . . Tintin! . . . You got him? . . . His trial begins tomorrow? . . . How long will it last? . . . Two days? . . . Good!

Two days later . . .
Venerable Master, Tintin is a prisoner of the Japanese and they've condemned him to death! . . . I saw posters in the city! . . .

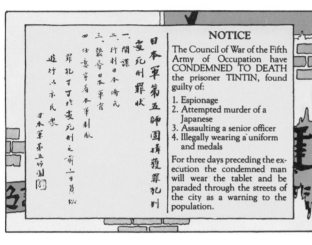
NOTICE

The Council of War of the Fifth Army of Occupation have CONDEMNED TO DEATH the prisoner TINTIN, found guilty of:

1. Espionage
2. Attempted murder of a Japanese
3. Assaulting a senior officer
4. Illegally wearing a uniform and medals

For three days preceding the execution the condemned man will wear the tablet and be paraded through the streets of the city as a warning to the population.

Three days go by . . .

Tomorrow at dawn Tintin ends his career . . . I can't see any way to get myself out of this one . . .

You really think he'll accept? . . . Seriously?

Now what do they want?

Hello, dear friend . . .

Mitsuhirato!

I come to you as a friend, dear Tintin . . . No, no I'm not joking. I've come to offer you your freedom!

Really?

Yes, but on two conditions. First, that you join our counter-espionage service. Second, that you tell me where you've hidden the poison you stole . . .

That's all?

That's all. Here are 10,000 dollars. You accept my proposition, I get you out tonight, and the money's yours . . .

He refused? . . .

How did you guess?

It's Mr Wang! . . .

How can I thank you?

Ssh! Not a sound! . . . We must hurry! . . . Follow me, quickly!

I'll lead the way . . .

Are you following me?

Yes, I'm behind you, Mr Wang.

There! . . . Now you're in my house!

Your house?

My house, yes . . . It's the one next to where you were imprisoned. As soon as I heard you'd been sentenced I rented this house. Then I made use of the three days you were being paraded to dig this tunnel . . .

We must leave the city at once. It will soon be light and the alarm will be raised . . . Ah, is everything ready?

Yes . . .

Vanished? The prisoner vanished? . . . Blockhead! . . . When you're guarding a prisoner you don't let him escape . . . And the major? . . . What's the major going to say?

Escaped? . . . Bungling blockheads! . . . When you're guarding a prisoner you watch him! . . . And the general? . . . What's the general going to say?

Blockheaded bungler! . . . When you're guarding important prisoners you're on your guard! . . . Now don't let this news get out!

Flaming Fujiyama! Tintin has escaped!

Double the guard on the gates . . . He can't be allowed to get out of the city. We'd be a laughing-stock! . . .

My brother told me, and he had it from one of the guards. Young Tintin escaped from prison, right under their noses!

Ah, so! That pest Tintin has escaped . . . I've got to keep my eyes open.

Where can he have gone?

Sergeant-major! ... The sentry! He's here ...

Hello? ... Yes ... What? ... Someone stole an armoured car? ... It isn't possible ... you must be mad! ... I ... Very well, I'm coming!

It's our lucky day! ... Everything went like clockwork! ...

Not to mention finding our brave Snowy wandering in the road ...

I've had enough! ... Enough, d'you hear? ... They'd steal a whole regiment, and all you'd see would be a puff of smoke!

Why didn't you go after them ... immediately? ... Answer me! ... Why not?

We ... we couldn't, General. All the other vehicles had been sabotaged ...

Then for heaven's sake, why didn't you send aeroplanes?

Three-quarters of an hour since they took off! What are they doing?

RRRRING

Yes, General ... We found the armoured car halted 12 miles away ... Yes, we landed and had a look ... Empty ... No, no one at all ... I don't know ... But sir ... Hello? ... Hello? ...

Bunglers, bunglers, bunglers! ... The lot of them! ... Who knows where Tintin is now?

Let's take it step by step. If we're going to save your son we must find Fang Hsi-ying. Then we'll take care of Mitsuhirato and his gang ...

I'm going tomorrow to Hukow, on the Yangtze Kiang. That's where the ransom for the professor is to be paid to the kidnappers.

The next morning . . .

Didn't you know? . . . The river has broken its banks . . . Everyone is fleeing from the floods . . . I doubt whether you will be able to reach Hukow at all . . .

What is happening?

The train isn't going any further. The line is cut . . .

Is it far to Hukow?

Three hours on foot . . .

Help! Help! Help!

He's alive!

That's better, eh? You almost swallowed half the river! . . . What's your name? . . . I'm Tintin . . .

I am Chang Chong-chen . . . But . . . why did you save my life?

?

I thought all white devils were wicked, like those who killed my grandfather and grandmother long ago. During the War of Righteous and Harmonious Fists, my father said.

The Boxer Rebellion, yes.

But Chang, all white men aren't wicked. You see, different peoples don't know enough about each other. Lots of Europeans still believe . . .

So you see Chang, that's what lots of people believe about China!

They must be crazy people in your country!!

Meanwhile . . .

I have news for you, General, about Tintin . . .

You know where he is?

. . . that all Chinese are cunning and cruel and wear pigtails, are always inventing tortures, and eating rotten eggs and swallows' nests . . .

The same stupid Europeans are quite convinced that all Chinese have tiny feet, and even now little Chinese girls suffer agonies with bandages . . .

. . . designed to prevent their feet developing normally. They're even convinced that Chinese rivers are full of unwanted babies, thrown in when they are born.

I have just received a telegram . . . He caught a train this morning for Hukow . . .

Hukow? . . . But that's deep into Chinese territory. So long as he's there we can't touch him . . .

Excuse me, General, there is one way . . . It's this . . .

Now, Chang, what are you going to do?

My parents are lost . . . I've nowhere to go . . . Couldn't I come with you? . . .

It's just . . . I may be running into great danger . . .

But two of us would be far stronger . . .

OK, then! . . . Off to Hukow!

I know a short cut . . .

What an excellent idea! ... It remains to be seen if the Chief of Police will agree ...

Oh, I can vouch for him, General ... Look ...

I, J. M. Dawson, Chief of Police of the International Settlement, owe the sum of 10,700 dollars to Mr Mitsuhirato

J. M. Dawson

Shanghai 18 . X . 31

Hee! Hee! Marvellous!

Next day ...

Mr Mitsuhirato? ... Very well, show him in ...

Good morning, Mr Mitsuhirato. What fair wind blows you here?

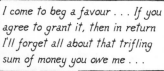

I come to beg a favour ... If you agree to grant it, then in return I'll forget all about that trifling sum of money you owe me ...

What are you getting at?

Quite simply ... Tintin is now in Hukow ... And I want you to get him arrested ...

Hukow? ... That's Chinese territory. My jurisdiction is limited to the International Settlement ...

Of course, but the Chinese wouldn't refuse you permission to go after a European, even outside the Settlement ...

No, maybe not ... But what reason can I give? ... Tintin hasn't committed any crime ...

A reason? ... How should I know? ... What if you suspect him of involvement in the kidnapping of Professor Fang Hsi-ying, for example ...

That's an idea ...

Chinese Police Head-quarters ... Good morning, Mr Dawson ... What? ... Fang Hsi-ying? ... You've got a lead? ... A European? And you want a pass for your detectives ... Of course ...

That's it ... We'll have the pass tomorrow morning. My men will leave as soon as it comes.

A happy arrangement. You arrest Tintin, and let him go for lack of evidence ... By chance, he falls into our hands ...

Right ... and you cancel that trifling debt of mine ...

Hukow ...

My father had a friend in the town ... We'll ask if we can stay with him ...

Of course . . . What greater happiness! My friend's son under my humble roof . . .

You already have travel permits. This is a safe-conduct from the Chinese authorities. It will facilitate your mission . . .

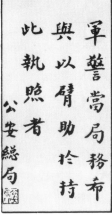

POLICE HEADQUARTERS

All Chinese authorities are hereby directed to render whatever assistance may be required by the bearer of this pass.

A rotten job!

Just our luck! . . . Ordered to arrest a friend!

There's a train later this evening. That gives us time to get ourselves ready . . .

Next morning . . .

What a life . . . All night in the train . . . then three hours' walk . . . Hukow at last . . .

Just as well we came in disguise . . .

Precisely!

Imagine the sensation we'd have caused, coming to a place like this in European clothes . . .

!

Don't look now, but something tells me we're being followed . . .

!

! ! ! !

Hey!! . . .

Goodness! . . . Gracious! . . .

Hello, what brings you here?

Poor soul, if only you knew . . . How to tell him? . . .

Come on, then . . . What's the matter?

Look at this.

A warrant for my arrest! . . .

And this . . . All Chinese authorities have to render assistance to the bearer of this pass . . .

All right, do what you must. I'm ready to go with you . . .

Goodbye, Chang. I'm being arrested. I have to go with them . . .

Now for the Chief of Police!

We've just arrested this young man, Your Honour. Here is our authorisation to operate in Chinese territory . . . Oh dear! Where's it gone?

Into the other pocket, obviously!

Goodness gracious! It isn't there either! . . . What . . .

I can't have put it away properly . . . I showed it to the prisoner . . .

Well, where is it?

What luck! . . . There it is!

Here it is! I found it!

!

? ?

Of course! I should have realised immediately.

What's so funny, Your Worship?

To be precise, why's he making fun of us?

You're funny, all right! . . . Ha! ha! ha! Here, you can have your precious paper . . . Then you'd better get out, fast! . . . Without your prisoner!

It's disgraceful!

We're a disgrace! . . .

It's . . . it's monstrous!

You'll hear more of this, Monstrosity!

We must do something!

We need something to do! Shanghai must be told!

As for you, young man, you're free to go, of course.

Thank you very much, Superintendent.

Here I am!

Free?

Yes, free . . . but I can't imagine why . . . The Superintendent took one look at the paper, roared with laughter, and threw the detectives out! . . . It's extraordinary, don't you think?

Not really. You see, I wrote the paper they showed to the Super-intendent . . . it was like this . . . The real document . . .

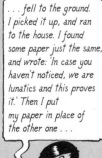

. . . fell to the ground. I picked it up, and ran to the house. I found some paper just the same, and wrote: 'In case you haven't noticed, we are lunatics and this proves it.' Then I put my paper in place of the other one . . .

Now I understand! . . . What a good friend you are, Chang!

Poor Thomson and Thompson!

Don't worry Tintin . . . They deserved it.

Kindly send this telegram to the Chief of Police, International Settlement, Shanghai . . .

Now we must look for Professor Fang Hsi-ying . . .

Yes, but there's a storm coming . . .

47

Botheration! Telegraph lines to Shanghai are cut because of the floods. We'll have to go ourselves . . .

To be precise . . . Shanghai will be flooded with telegrams because we cut ourselves . . .

Here's the storm . . . I think we'd be safer to go back down . . .

You're right, Chang . . .

Meanwhile, in Hukow . . .

Here's my messenger! . . . You've got news of Tintin's arrest, that's for sure!

'Arrest failed. Tintin free. Instructions awaited.' Seventy-seven suffering Samurais!

I want this finished! Desperate cases call for desperate remedies! 'Liquidate!' One word, that's enough!

What a beastly business . . . travelling all night . . .

All because of that rotten commissar! . . .

The next morning . . .

That's the old temple they mean . . .

A lot of tourists must visit this old temple. Look, Chang, there's even a photographer . . .

Picture of you together, gentlemen? Ready in five minutes . . .

OK?

If you like . . .

Ready now . . . Watch the birdie! . . .

BANG
BANG
BANG

48

Infernal machine! My tommy-gun jammed! . . .

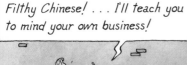
Filthy Chinese! . . . I'll teach you to mind your own business!

Hands up, gangster, or I'll 'photograph' you at point blank range!

Now then, start talking! Japanese, aren't you? . . . Mitsuhirato put you up to this, didn't he?

Yes, he's afraid of you . . . You have the Rajaijah poison. If you find Fang Hsi-ying, he thinks the professor will develop an antidote . . . That's why he kidnapped the professor . . .

So that was him, too! What about the letter accusing Chinese gangsters?

The ransom letter was a fake to lead the police on a false trail.

A fake! I should have guessed it!

So Professor Fang Hsi-ying is not in the old temple . . . Where is he?

I don't know.

That's a lie!

It's the truth! I swear! . . . Only Mitsuhirato knows where the professor is . . .

All right, we'll go back down to Hukow . . . Nothing serious, is it, Chang?

No, luckily the bullet only grazed your shoulder.

The Chinese police can handle this thug . . .

That's put him behind bars . . . Now, Chang, if Mitsuhirato won't come to us, we'll go to Mitsuhirato! . . . What do you think?

I agree!

All right, off we go to Shanghai!

That's the Shanghai train coming now . . .

Here we are again.

To be precise: here we aren't. It's three hours, walk to Hukow . . . What a life, Thomson, what a life!

I was behind him . . . I saw him trip over the suitcase and fall on the platform. Just a silly accident.

Ah! He's beginning to come round . . .

TINTIN!

What about Tintin? . . .

On the platform! . . . Waiting for the train!

The train! It's leaving for Shanghai . . .

Great snakes! Thomson! . . . Let's hope he doesn't catch us! . . .

. . . I was just catching it, but I didn't notice I'd run out of platform! . . .

Only one thing to do: warn Shanghai by telegram. They'll arrest him on arrival . . .

Next morning...

That's the last of the passengers ... and still no sign of Tintin ...

No luck, Chief ... He wasn't on the train. I reckon he hopped off en route ...

Infuriating! Wretched little brat! ... Always outwits us at the last minute!

It's dark now ... We can risk it ...

Good thing we jumped when the train slowed outside the station. I'm sure someone would have been waiting at the barrier ...

Mr Mitsuhirato? ... Yes, it's me ... I'm afraid not ... slipped through our fingers! ... Yes, I'm as sorry as you are ... What do you expect? I did my best ...

Policemen! ... I suppose I'll have to do it myself, for the umpteenth time!

Come in!

RAT TAT TAT

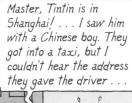
Master, Tintin is in Shanghai! ... I saw him with a Chinese boy. They got into a taxi, but I couldn't hear the address they gave the driver ...

Pity! ... Listen, Yamato ... Get busy ... Try to discover where he's gone to ground, and who's hiding him. Understand?

Yes

The gods be praised! We meet again! ... You must rest for a few days ... Give your wound a chance to heal ...

I will ... Then we must deal with Mitsu—hirato!

A week later ...

You're sure it doesn't hurt any more?

Not a bit, Chang ... Look, all back to normal ...

That night ...

There's Mitsuhirato's house. While I get inside, you keep guard ...

OK ...

No one! ... So far so good ...

You're sure Tintin is there right now? ...

Why shouldn't he be? ... He's been there for over a week ...

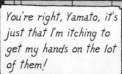

You're right, Yamato, it's just that I'm itching to get my hands on the lot of them!

All clear: you can come ...

What's the matter? ... You seem worried ...

I'll explain later, Chang ... Hurry! We haven't a moment to lose ...

A car, quickly! We need a car!

At last ... there's one now ...

Quick, driver, quick! ... Take us to the Nanking road!

Look here, I'm not a taxi! ... Can't you see this is a private car?

Doesn't matter! For heaven's sake get going! ... Please! ... Lives are at stake!

No, no, no! ... And when I say no I mean no!

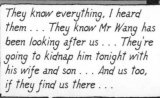

They know everything, I heard them ... They know Mr Wang has been looking after us ... They're going to kidnap him tonight with his wife and son ... And us too, if they find us there ...

Shall we be in time?

All seems quiet . . .

The door isn't closed! . . .

It's Mr Wang's servant! . . . He's been chloroformed!

Too late! They've been kidnapped!

The game's up, Mr Wang! . . . You are all in my power! . . . There's only Tintin . . . In a few hours he too will have ceased to annoy me! . . .

Tintin! . . .

?

Look what I've found . . .

!

Blue Lotus

Wang.

Come on!

To the Blue Lotus!

The Blue Lotus? . . . It's an opium den in Shanghai . . . How do I get in without being recognised? . . . In disguise? . . .

Will there be anything more, sir?

No, no thank you . . .

He is here . . .

You're sure it's him?

Indeed, Master . . . He has tried to disguise himself . . . A fake beard and a black wig, but I recognised him . . .

Now for some fun! . . .

WHEEET

Oh, my goodness! Someone seems to have a bone to pick with me!

BANG

That's it! . . . Let him have it!

OH!

THUMP

BANG

YEOW

Not a bad idea, was it, my friend? . . . That trick with the little bit of paper, with a scrawl on it by Mr Wang . . .

I protest! . . . I . . . I protest! . . .

Hee! Hee! You protest! . . . You've got a nerve, I must say!

OW! . . .

?

YEOW!

?

Fujiyama! . . . Not Tintin! . . . Untie him! . . .

No, I am not Tintin! I am the Consul for Poldavia! . . . You'll hear more of this, villain!

Forgive me, sir, it was all a mistake . . . I took you for somebody else . . .

Even for somebody else, that's no way to treat people! . . . You will pay dearly for this!

Seven hundred suffering Samurais! . . . Wait till I get him, just wait till I get him!

I'm going home! . . . Yamato, be ready with the lorry at midnight tomorrow, at godown No. 9. The 'Harika Maru' will moor alongside. Load the goods and take them to the warehouse . . .

Yes, Master . . .

Goodbye! . . . Telephone me if there are any developments . . .

Right, Master . . .

I don't think Tintin will come . . .

No, he'll be suspicious . . .

Ha! Ha! None of that fell on deaf ears! . . .

THE BLUE LOTUS

Any news?

All's well, Chang. I discovered quite a lot . . . Come quickly, we mustn't stay here . . . I'll put you in the picture . . .

Midnight tomorrow? . . . I'll come with you . . .

No, Chang, I think it's better if I go alone . . . I'll tell you why . . .

The next night . . .

Careful, there they are!

Is that the last lot?

Yes, just these to be loaded, and we can go . . . .

So far so good . . .

Take the opium out of the barrel, get inside . . . and Bob's your uncle . . .

OK, we can move off now . . .

Meanwhile . . .

It was a mistake to pit your wits against mine, my dear Wang! . . . A big mistake! . . . But it's too late now . . . The time has come for you to die!

You smile? . . . You think it's like a thriller, don't you? . . . The hero rushes in at the last moment and saves your life . . . Pardon my laughter! . . . At this very moment your hero Tintin is already in my power!

We've been going for two hours . . . I wonder where to . . .

So you can abandon all hope! . . . They say the Chinese aren't afraid to die. Well, I've prepared a fitting end for you! . . . Your son, Wang, your own mad son, will cut off your head! . . . Picture the scene . . . Your wife, Tintin, and you, all beheaded by your son! . . .

Ah, it's you, Yamato! . . . All went well?

Like clockwork, Master . . . The barrels are in there . . .

Please enter, dear Mr Wang! . . . We don't want you to miss the show!

Now for some fun!

That's the one, Master . . . marked with a cross . . .

My dear Tintin, welcome to the end of the road!

Something tells me you weren't expecting this sort of reception when you emerged!

Too true!

I knew perfectly well you were in the barrel . . . You were at the Blue Lotus last night . . . and had a good laugh at my expense, no doubt . . . You heard the orders I gave Yamato . . . Everything had gone your way . . . But one of my men saw you leave and alerted me.

I told myself you certainly wouldn't be able to resist such a good opportunity, so I set a trap. I told them to leave you alone, they loosened the top of one barrel, and everything happened as I'd foreseen!

Well done, Mr Mitsuhirato. You're quite a clever man!

Cleverer than you thought, anyway! . . . Ah, here's an old friend of yours . . . He doesn't want to miss your execution! . . .

?

We got him, Grand Master.

Mr Rastapopoulos!

Exactly!

Rastapopoulos! . . . Roberto Rastapopoulos! You've been trying to spike my guns for a long time . . . Me, Rastapopoulos, king of drug-smugglers . . . Rastapopoulos, who went over a cliff near Gaipajama . . . and you thought I died . . . Rastapopoulos, alive and well . . . And as always, coming out on top . . .

You, leader of the gang? . . . Impossible!

Bring in the others, Yamato . . .

You aren't convinced, eh? . . . Look at that! . . . Now do you believe me? . . .

The sign of the Pharaoh Kih-Oskh!*

Here, take this. It's for you . . .

Lao Tzu said: 'You must find the way' . . . I've found it . . . It's quite easy. I'm going to cut off your head. Then you too will know the truth . . .

You're . . . you're absolutely sure there isn't any risk for us? . . .

No, as soon as he's done the job Yamato will take care of him . . .

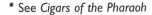

* See Cigars of the Pharaoh

THE SHANGHAI NEWS
上海報

FANG HSI-YING FOUND!
PROFESSOR PRISONER IN OPIUM DEN!

SHANGHAI, Wednesday: Professor Fang Hsi-ying has been found! The good news was flashed to us this morning.

Last week eminent scholar Fang disappeared on his way home from a party given by a friend. Police efforts to trace him were unavailing. No clues were found.

Young European reporter Tintin joined in the hunt for the missing man of science. Earlier we reported incidents involving Tintin and the occupying Japanese forces. Secret society Sons of the Dragon aided Tintin in the rescue. Fang Hsi-ying was kidnapped by an international

Professor Fang Hsi-ying pictured just after his release.

gang of drug-smugglers, now all safely in police custody.

A wireless transmitter was found by police at the Blue Lotus opium den. The transmitter was used by the drug-smugglers to communicate wth their ships on the high seas. Information radioed included sea routes, ports to be avoided, points of embarkation and uploading.

Home of Japanese subject Mitsuhirato was also searched. No comment, say police on reports of seizure of top-secret documents. Unconfirmed rumours suggest the papers concern undercover political activity by a neighbouring power. Speculation mounts that they disclose the recent Shanghai-Nanking railway incident as a pretext for extended Japanese occupation. League of Nations officials in Geneva will study the captured documents.

TINTIN'S OWN STORY

This morning, hero of the hour, Mr Tintin, talked to us about his adventures.

Tintin, rescuer of Professor Fang Hsi-ying, with Snowy, his faithful companion.

The young reporter is the guest of Mr Wang Chen-yee at his host's picturesque villa on the Nanking road. When we called, our hero, young and smiling, greeted us wearing Chinese dress. Could this really be the scourge of the terrible Shanghai gangsters?

After our greetings and congratulations, we asked Mr Tintin to tell us how he succeeded in smashing the most dangerous organisation.

Mr Wang, a tall, elderly, venerable

man with an impish smile, said:

"You must tell the world it is entirely due to him that my wife, my son and I are alive today!"

With these words our interview was concluded, and we said farewell to the friendly reporter and his kindly host.

L.G.T.

Young people carry posters of Tintin through Shanghai streets.

The conclusions of the Sub-Committee leave no room for doubt. The documents seized in Shanghai provide irrefutable proof. The attack upon the Shanghai-Nanking railway was planned and executed by a Japanese subject working upon direct orders from his government! . . .

I shall be interested to hear the Japanese delegate's reply . . .

Me, too . . . Look, he's going to speak now . . .

Gentlemen, make no mistake! I categorically deny the accusations contained in the report of the 873rd Sub-Committee. These accusations are an insult to which Japan declines to make any response other than silence and contempt! Nevertheless, to prove that the integrity of my country is beyond doubt . . .

. . . I am authorised to announce that my government has ordered its troops to withdraw from Chinese territories occupied after the incident on the Shanghai-Nanking railway. To that, gentlemen, I must add with regret that in solemn protest against the affront to my country, Japan finds herself obliged to resign from the League of Nations!

WAY OUT

Meanwhile, in Shanghai . . .

I have wonderful news for you: my son is cured! . . . Professor Fang Hsi-ying has discovered an antidote to the terrible poison of madness! . . .

He has? . . . Oh, how glad I am!

Venerable Master, two gentlemen wish to speak to Mr Tintin.

Some days later...

...I raise my glass to your precious health, Tintin. Your courage and nobility have restored happiness to this humble house. Your memory will be engraved upon our hearts as in the finest crystal...

There is one who, if such is possible, will miss you even more than I. Chang, who has already known the sadness of losing his parents. Chang, who found in you a brother. If he wishes, he will be my son, the brother of my own poor son to whom our honourable friend Fang Hsi-ying has restored his reason...

What is the matter, Chang?

There is a rainbow in my heart, Venerable Lady ...I weep because Tintin is going but the sun shines because I have a new mother and father!

Farewell, noble Tintin. May other friendships lighten your days in your country in the West, and accompany you along the way!

The next morning...

Goodbye, Tintin... Good luck go with you!

I wish the same for you, Chang! ...Goodbye!

TOOOOT

TOOOOT